THE
Christmas
Mice

With 12 Christmas cards
to Open and a Game to Play

Written by Caroline Repchuk

Illustrated by Stephanie Boey

TEMPLAR

Underneath a wide oak tree in the middle of the wood lived a wise old mouse, Great Grandpa Mousekins. It was a cold winter's day, and he shivered as he pulled his old blanket around him and sat back deep in thought.

He wanted this to be the best Christmas ever, so he was planning a grand celebration. He sent out Christmas cards to all of his family, and written on the back, in little spindly writing, was a special invitation.

Cousin Alice was delighted
when her invitation arrived.
She had not been looking forward
to Christmas on her own.
She decided to reply at once and
ran to the mailbox with her card.

Beneath a hedge at the edge of a field,
Fern and Flower, the little fieldmice twins,
were so excited that they both wanted
to write to Great Grandpa.

Behind the baseboard upstairs in the Big House, Harriet the house mouse was just checking to make sure there was no sign of the cat before going out to mail her reply when Bert from the kitchen appeared. "I'll mail yours for you," he said, and tucked her reply under his arm.

As Christmas Eve drew near,
Bill the mailman delivered more
cards to Great Grandpa's
house each day.

Everyone was eager to come.
The old mouse smiled as he
thought of the surprise he had
in store for them all...

Deep in his burrow, far underground,
Dozy Dormouse stayed awake just long
enough to write his reply.

Luckily his friend Harvey the
harvest mouse had come to collect it,
on his way to the mailbox.

At last the great day arrived,
and all the family gathered
from far and wide in
Great Grandpa Mousekins'
cosy home beneath
the old oak tree.
But what was this?
Great Grandpa Mousekins
was nowhere to be seen!

On the mantelpiece was a letter,
addressed to *'all the family'*.

Imagine everyone's surprise when Great Grandpa
Mousekins appeared from the chimney, dressed as
'Father Christmouse', and carrying a large sack of gifts!

How they laughed at his gray whiskers all covered with soot. In his sack he had just the right present for each of them. What a lovely surprise!

But the biggest surprise of all
was for Great Grandpa Mousekins
himself! All the family had joined
together to make him an extra special
Christmas gift.

Look carefully back through
the story, and see if you can guess
what it is. The answer is in
the envelope opposite.

A day of fun and feasting
was had by one and all, and
Great Grandpa Mousekins
said it was the best
Christmas ever!